Streamline ENGLISH

BERNARD HARTLEY & PETER VINEY

CONNECTIONS

WORKBOOK A
UNITS 1–40

Oxford University Press

Oxford University Press
Walton Street, Oxford OX2 6DP

Oxford   New York
Toronto   Melbourne
Auckland   Cape Town   Nairobi
Dar es Salaam   Petaling Jaya
Singapore   Hong Kong   Tokyo
Delhi   Bombay   Calcutta
Madras   Karachi

and associated companies in
Beirut Berlin Ibadan Nicosia

OXFORD is a trademark of
Oxford University Press

ISBN 0 19 432235 1 (workbook A)
ISBN 0 19 432236 X (workbook B)
ISBN 0 19 432227 0 (complete
student's edition)

© Bernard Hartley and Peter Viney 1981

First published 1981
Eleventh impression 1987

Illustrations by:
Paddy Mounter

Printed in Great Britain
at the University Printing House, Oxford
by David Stanford
Printer to the University

To the teacher

Workbook A of *Streamline English Connections* consists of forty units. Each unit relates directly to the equivalent unit in *Streamline English Connections* Units 1–40.

The *Workbook* is an optional element of the course, designed to provide language summaries and additional written exercises. It may be used in the following ways:

1   In more extensive courses as additional classroom material, providing extra oral practice and written reinforcement and consolidation of the basic core material in the student's edition.

2   As material for homework in more intensive situations.

The *Workbook* should only be used after full oral practice of the corresponding unit in the student's edition. The language summaries provide material for revision.

A further workbook is available for units 41–80 of the student's edition, under the title *Workbook B*.

Bernard Hartley
Peter Viney

Unit 1 (Revision)

Exercise 1

A She's Scottish.
B *She isn't Scottish.*
C *Is she Scottish?*

Now do the same.

1 A They come from Stirling.

   B ....

   C ....

2 A They've been to Genoa.

   B ....

   C ....

3 A He works in a bank.

   B ....

   C ....

4 A They're going to Corfu.

   B ....

   C ....

5 A They went to Gibraltar.

   B ....

   C ....

6 A There's a shower in the cabin.

   B ....

   C ....

Exercise 2

Complete this.

I	me	my	mine
1 you	....	....	....
2	him	....	....
3	....	her	....
4 it	....	....	....
5	....	our	....
6	....	....	theirs

Exercise 3

1 *January is the first month.*
2 *February is the second month.*

3 March ....

4 ....

5 ....

6 ....

7 ....

8 ....

9 ....

10 ....

11 ....

12 ....

Exercise 4

You're at a party. Complete this conversation.

A Hello. What's your name?

B ....

A Where do you come from?

B ....

A Where's that?

B ....

A What do you do?

B ....

A Would you like a drink?

B ....

A With lemon?

B ....

Unit 2 (Revision)

Exercise 1

Look at the first conversation in the student's book.
Write a conversation using this information.

```
Addresses/Telephone Numbers

Harry Morgan,
32 Paramount Street,
Southampton    (0703) 184351
```

A ....

B ....

A ....

B ....

A ....

B ....

....

A ....

B ....

A ....

B ....

Exercise 2

Look at the third conversation in the student's book. You are
going to make a transferred charge call to your home, or to a
friend's home.
Complete this conversation.

A Number please?

B ....

A Where to?

B ....

A And what number?

B ....

A What's your name?

B ....

A Could you spell it?

B ....

A What number are you calling from?

B ....

A O.K. Hold on, please.

Exercise 3

Who are you telephoning? *Nobody.*

Continue. You can use these words:
nobody/none/nowhere/nothing.

1 What are you doing?

....

2 Where are you going?

....

3 Who are you talking to?

....

4 How many did you get?

....

Exercise 4

Look at this information. You are in Bournemouth. These are
the call charges for different towns:

Poole (L)   Dorchester (a)   Plymouth (b)
Christchurch (L) Salisbury (a)   Nottingham (b)

Poole, Tuesday, 11 a.m., 6 minutes. *12p.*

Now write down the price of these calls.

1 Plymouth, Sunday, 2 minutes 10 seconds.

....

2 Dorchester, Thursday, 8.30 a.m., 4 minutes

....

3 Christchurch, Wednesday, 12.15 p.m., 1 minute 30 seconds.

....

4 Nottingham, Friday, 2 p.m., 2 minutes 30 seconds.

....

5 Salisbury, Saturday, 6 minutes.

....

6 Dorchester, Monday, 5.30 p.m., 4 minutes 30 seconds.

....

Inland call charges *from ordinary lines*

From exchanges with STD facilities

	Dialled direct Time allowed for 4p in any one call
Peak rate (Mon-Fri 9 am-1 pm)	
L local	2 min.
a up to 56 km	30 sec.
b over 56 km	10 sec.
Standard rate (Mon-Fri 8 am-9 am/1 pm-6 pm)	
L local	3 min.
a up to 56 km	45 sec.
b over 56 km	15 sec.
Cheap rate (All other times)	
L local	12 min.
a up to 56 km	3 min.
b over 56 km	1 min.

Unit 3 (Revision)

Exercise 1

A *I can see some difference.*
B *I can't see any difference.*
C *Can you see any difference?*

Now do the same.

1 A She has to do some washing.

B ....

C ....

2 A She washed the clothes.

B ....

C ....

3 A They've washed the clothes.

B ....

C ....

4 A She's got some young children.

B ....

C ....

5 A She's going to buy "Fizz".

B ....

C ....

6 A They take their clothes to the launderette.

B ....

....

C ....

....

Exercise 2

white ... whiter ... whitest

Complete this.

1 soft ....

2 .... cleaner ....

3 .... better ....

4 bad ....

5 .... more expensive ....

6 .... least expensive

Exercise 3

It's a good wine. (he) *It's the best wine he's ever drunk.*

Continue.

1 It's a good book. (I) ....

2 It's an exciting film. (they) ....

3 It's a fast car. (she) ....

4 It's a bad film. (we) ....

5 It's a good washing powder. (I) ....

6 It's interesting music. (he) ....

Exercise 4

This is big *but that's bigger.*
These are dirty *but those are dirtier.*

Continue.

1 This is good ....

2 These are bad ....

3 These are interesting ....

4 This is cheap ....

5 This is large ....

6 These are expensive ....

Unit 4 (Revision)

Language summary

I/You He/She We/They	went didn't go did not go	there	yesterday. last week. in 1966. at two o'clock. on Monday.	Did	I/you he/she we/they	go	there?	Yes, I did. No, I didn't.

I You We They	've have haven't have not	gone.	Have	I you we they	gone?	Yes, we have. No, they haven't.
He She	's has hasn't has not		Has	he she		Yes, he has. No, she hasn't.

Look at this

begin-began-begun	go-went-gone	jump-jumped-jumped	slip-slipped-slipped
crash-crashed-crashed	get-got-got	land-landed-landed	swim-swam-swum
dive-dived-dived	hit-hit-hit	lift-lifted-lifted	throw-threw-thrown
finish-finished-finished	hold-held-held	make-made-made	win-won-won
fall-fell-fallen	hurt-hurt-hurt	run-ran-run	

Exercise 1

A *He swam 100 metres.*
B *She didn't swim 100 metres.*
C *Did they swim 100 metres?*

Now do the same

1 A He fell.

   B ....

   C ....

2 A ....

   B She didn't slip.

   C ....

3 A ....

   B She didn't begin it.

   C ....

4 A ....

   B ....

   C Did they make it?

5 A ....

   B ....

   C Did they finish?

6 A He won.

   B ....

   C ....

Exercise 2

A *He's begun.*
B *She hasn't begun.*
C *Have they begun?*

1 A ....

   B ....

   C Have they fallen?

2 A He's slipped.

   B ....

   C ....

3 A ....

   B She hasn't swum 100 metres.

   C ....

4 A ....

   B ....

   C Have they made it?

5 A He's finished.

   B ....

   C ....

6 A ....

   B She hasn't won.

   C ....

Exercise 3

Women's 100 metres.
Green 11.58 seconds
Foster 11.55 seconds
Foster ran faster than Green.

Continue.

1 *Men's swimming:*
200 metres freestyle.
Davis 1 minute 61 seconds
Brown 1 minute 54 seconds

....

....

2 *Women's high jump.*
Gold 1.92 metres
Harlow 1.91 metres

....

....

3 *Men's 1500 metres.*
Thomas 3 minutes 41 seconds
Horne 3 minutes 42 seconds

....

....

4 *Men's 100 metres.*
Walls 10.5 seconds
Jones 10.8 seconds

....

....

Unit 5 (Revision)

Language summary

I	'll	be	there	tomorrow.	Will	I	be	there?	Yes, I will.
You	will			next week.		you			No, I won't.
He	won't			next year.		he			
She	will not			next month.		she			
It				next Monday.		it			
We				at two o'clock.		we			
They				later.		they			

Exercise 1

He/Tuesday/Sunday
He'll be here next Tuesday, but he won't be here next Sunday.

Continue.

1 I/three o'clock/seven o'clock

....

....

2 She/Wednesday/Saturday

....

....

3 They/next week/next month

....

....

4 We/later/tomorrow

....

....

5 He/two o'clock/eight o'clock

....

....

6 I/Friday/weekend

....

....

Exercise 2

A He's here this morning.
B *He was here yesterday morning.*
C *He'll be here tomorrow morning.*

Continue.

1 A They're here today.

B ....

C ....

2 A We're here tonight.

B ....

C ....

3 A You're here this week.

B ....

C ....

4 A She's here this evening.

B ....

C ....

5 A It's here this afternoon.

B ....

C ....

6 A He's here this month.

B ....

C ....

Exercise 3

He/on Wednesday   *Will he be here on Wednesday?*
Continue.

1 They/next week

....

2 It/later

....

3 You/tomorrow

....

4 She/at 4.30

....

Unit 6

Language summary

I/You	'll	go there.	Will	I/you	go there?	Yes, he will.
He/She/It	will	do it.		he/she/it	do it?	No, we won't.
We/They	won't	see them.		we/they	see them?	
	will not	eat it.			eat it?	

Exercise 1

Complete this.

Every day	Yesterday	Tomorrow .....
he catches the train.	he caught the train.	he'll catch the train.
1 they get up at seven o'clock.	....	....
2	she went to the supermarket.	....
3	....	we'll have dinner at 7.30.
4 she meets him at the station.	....	....
5	....	he'll take the dog for a walk.
6	they washed up.	....

Exercise 2

I'll walk to school.
I won't go to the discothèque.

Now, write sentences about tomorrow.

1 .... play tennis.

2 .... go to school.

3 .... clean the house.

4 .... read a newspaper.

5 .... cook a meal.

6 .... interview Miss World.

7 .... watch television.

8 .... meet Paul McCartney.

Exercise 3

What *time will he have dinner?* He'll have dinner at seven.

1 Where ....?

She'll go to New York.

2 Who ....?

He'll meet Jane Fonda.

3 What ....?

They'll play football.

4 When ....?

He'll take his exams next year.

5 How many ....?

They'll buy three books.

6 How much ....?

It'll cost $10,000.

Exercise 4

Will you get up at seven o'clock tomorrow? *Yes, I will.*
Will you have tea with breakfast? *No, I won't.*

Now write true answers.

1 Will you have a bath tomorrow?

....

2 Will you watch television tomorrow?

....

3 Will you interview Miss World?

....

4 Will you come to school on Saturday?

....

5 Will you wash up this evening?

....

6 Will you go home by bus tomorrow?

....

Unit 7

Language summary

| He's / She's | one of the | busiest / most important | men / women | in the | world. / country. |

| He / They | 'll / will | be here | for / until | two days./three weeks. / Saturday./August 20th. |

Exercise 1

He's very busy. *He's one of the busiest men in the world.*
Continue.

1 She's very important ....

2 He's very rich. ....

3 She's very intelligent. ....

4 He's very strong. ....

5 She's very beautiful. ....

Exercise 2

He/Saturday   *He'll be here until Saturday.*
They/three hours   *They'll be here for three hours.*
Continue.

1 She/three o'clock

....

2 We/January 13th

....

3 I/Thursday

....

4 They/two days

....

5 You/ten minutes

....

6 We/several days

....

7 I/next Sunday

....

8 She/five hours

....

Exercise 3

Look at Unit 7 of the Student's book.
This is Dr. Sowanso's itinerary for August.

Aug. 10 Bonn/Germany/Chancellor/Europe
Aug. 13 Lagos/Nigeria/President/Africa
Aug. 17 Riyadh/Saudi Arabia/King/Middle East

Aug. 22 Tokyo/Japan/Prime Minister/Asia
Aug. 25 Ottawa/Canada/Prime Minister/North America
Aug. 31 Brasilia/Brazil/President/South America

On August 10th he'll be in Bonn. He'll meet the German Chancellor. They'll discuss European affairs.

Now describe the rest of his journey.

1 ....

....

....

2 ....

....

3 ....

....

4 ....

....

....

5 ....

....

Unit 8 (Revision)

I You We They	always usually sometimes rarely never	sleep	well. badly.	Do	I you we they	always usually ever	sleep	well? badly?
He She		sleeps		Does	he she			

Look at this

dream-dreamt-dreamt   sleep-slept-slept
get up-got up-got up   feed-fed-fed
stand-stood-stood   meet-met-met

Exercise 1

Complete these.

1 need   ....   6 sleep   ....
2 ....   began   ....   7 ....   fed   ....
3 ....   hurt   8 ....   thrown
4 swim   ....   9 ....   fallen
5 ....   stood

Exercise 2

A *Have you ever done it?*
B *Yes, I have.*
A *When did you do it?*

Complete these conversations.

1 A Have you ever been to London?

  B Yes, I have.

  A When ....?

2 A ....

  ....?

  B Yes, I have.

  A Where did you see an accident?

3 A ....

  ....?

  B Yes, I have.

  A Why did you fall out of bed?

4 A ....

  ....?

  B Yes, I have.

  A Which important person did you meet?

5 A Have you ever hit anybody?

  B Yes, I have.

  A Who ....?

6 A Have you ever found any money?

  B Yes, I have.

  A How much ....?

Exercise 3

Answer these questions.

1 How many hours' sleep do you need?

  ....

2 What time do you usually go to bed?

  ....

3 What time do you usually get up?

  ....

4 What time did you go to bed last night?

  ....

5 What time did you get up this morning?

  ....

6 Did you sleep well or badly last night?

  ....

7 Have you ever walked in your sleep?

  ....

8 Have you ever had a nightmare?

  ....

Unit 9

Look at this

pill

tablet

capsule

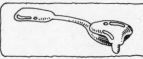
a spoonful of medicine

Exercise 1

Look at the first conversation in the student's book. Write a similar conversation, using these words: bad sore throat/a couple of days/this medicine/two spoonfuls/twice a day.

A Good morning.

B ....

A ....

B ....

A ....

B ....

....

A ....

Exercise 2

You want a new hairbrush. The shop has got nylon and natural bristle, and several colours. Look at the second conversation and write a similar one.

A ....

B ....

....

A ....

B ....

A ....

....

B ....

....

A ....

Exercise 3

Look at the third conversation.

glue

chocolate

biscuits

jam

tissues

sticking-plaster

beans

shampoo

Could I have a tube of glue, please?

Write sentences.

1 ....

2 ....

3 ....

4 ....

5 ....

6 ....

7 ....

Exercise 4

pay now/later   *Shall I pay now or later?*

Continue.

1 do it tomorrow/the day after tomorrow

....

2 give it to you at lunchtime/this afternoon

....

3 finish it now/in a few minutes

....

4 go now/at three o'clock

Unit 10

Language summary

I/You We/They	want don't want	it. them. him. her.		I/You We/They	want don't want	to	do it. see them. meet him. talk to her.
He She	wants doesn't want			He She	wants doesn't want		

I You We They	want don't want	me you him her it us them	to	do it. see them. meet him. talk to her.
He She	wants doesn't want			

What Who	do you want?
What	do you want to do?
What	do you want her to do?

Exercise 1

Pam Adams is a Grand Prix racing driver. She's talking to a reporter at the beginning of the new motor-racing season. "I want to win this race. I want to be the fastest and best driver. I want to be the world champion. I want to retire after this season. I don't want to race next year. I want to stay at home, and I want to watch the races on T.V.!"

She wants to win this race.

Write six sentences.

1 ....

2 ....

3 ....

4 ....

5 ....

6 ....

Exercise 2

Lord Worth is an English aristocrat. Charles is his butler and he wants the servants to do several things today. He's made a list.

Mary and Anne (maids)

clean the rooms
hoover the carpets
prepare the guest-room
wash up

Mrs Bridges (cook)

prepare a special dinner
cook roast beef
make an apple pie
bake a cake

James (chauffeur)

wash the Rolls
polish it
check the oil and water
take Lord Worth to the airport

Mary and Anne: *He wants them to clean the rooms.*
Mrs Bridges: *He wants her to prepare a special dinner.*
James: *He wants him to wash the Rolls.*

Now write three sentences about Mary and Anne, about Mrs Bridges and James.

Mary and Anne	Mrs Bridges	James
1	1	1 ....
....	....	....
2	2	2 ....
....	....	....
3	3	3 ....
....	....	....

Unit 11

Exercise 1

sweet   *sour*
rich   *poor*

Now write in the opposites. Use these words: expensive/stale/old/better/ boring/thin/easy/old/bad/unhappy/big/ beautiful/light/thin/right/soft/strong/ uncomfortable/clean/cool/dry/cold/fast/ short.

1 good   ....

2 cheap   ....

3 comfortable   ....

4 warm   ....

5 hot   ....

6 fresh   ....

7 happy   ....

8 interesting   ....

9 young   ....

10 new   ....

11 left   ....

12 hard   ....

13 worse   ....

14 weak   ....

15 tall   ....

16 ugly   ....

17 small   ....

18 dirty   ....

19 difficult   ....

20 wet   ....

21 slow   ....

22 heavy   ....

23 thick   ....

24 fat   ....

Exercise 2

Pierre Lebrun/Switzerland
A *Your name sounds French.*
B *Yes, but I'm not French. I'm Swiss.*

Continue.

1 Miguel Gonzalez/Mexico

  A ....

  B ....

2 John Smith/Australia

  A ....

  B ....

3 Fritz Schmidt/Austria

  A ....

  B ....

4 Luigi Gordini/United States

  A ....

  B ....

Exercise 3

This perfume's lovely. *Yes, it smells lovely.*
This room's warm. *Yes, it feels warm.*

Continue.

1 That record's loud.

....

2 This beef's excellent.

....

3 That house is modern.

....

4 These vegetables are fresh.

....

5 That radiator's hot.

....

6 This coat's expensive.

....

7 This music's very good.

....

8 These flowers are nice.

....

9 This cheese is awful.

....

Unit 12 (Revision)

Look at this

fly – flew – flown	switch – switched – switched
say – said – said	breathe – breathed – breathed
put – put – put	reply – replied – replied
understand – understood – understood	step – stepped – stepped
stick – stuck – stuck	

Exercise 1

Complete these.

1 is ....

2 .... were ....

3 hit ....

4 .... stood ....

5 take off ....

6 .... put on ....

7 stop ....

8 carry ....

9 descend ....

10 .... snored ....

11 use ....

12 .... said

Exercise 2

"We can't see the surface of the planet."
They couldn't see the surface of the planet.

Continue.

1 "We can breathe the air."

....

2 "We can't find any intelligent life."

....

3 "We can't start the engines."

....

4 "We can't take off."

....

5 "We can take off our helmets."

....

Exercise 3

Complete these.

something	anything	nothing	everything
1	anywhere	....	....
2	....	no one	....
3	....	....	everybody
4 some	....	....	....

Exercise 4

clouds *There were too many white clouds.*
noise *There was too much noise.*

Continue.

1 people

....

2 traffic

....

3 cars

....

4 buses

....

5 pollution

....

6 smoke

....

Unit 13

Language summary

It's too hot for me to drink.
It's cool enough for me to drink.
I'm not strong enough to lift it.
I'm too weak to lift it.

catch – caught – caught
forget – forgot – forgotten
leave – left – left
bring – brought – brought

Exercise 1

It's very hot. I can't drink it.   *It's too hot for me to drink.*

Continue.

1 It's very expensive. We can't buy it.

....

2 It's very heavy. They can't carry it.

....

3 It's very high. He can't touch it.

....

4 It's very sweet. She can't drink it.

....

5 It's very dirty. I can't clean it.

....

6 It's very quiet. You can't hear it.

....

Exercise 2

They're cheap. I can buy them.   *They're cheap enough for me to buy.*

Continue.

1 It's loud. They can hear it.

....

2 It's easy. We can understand it.

....

3 They're light. He can lift them.

....

4 It's cool. They can drink it.

....

5 It's easy. You can do it.

....

6 They're good. I can use them.

....

Exercise 3

He can't drive it. He isn't old enough.   *He isn't old enough to drive it.*

Continue.

1 She can't carry them. She isn't strong enough.

....

2 We can't buy it. We aren't rich enough.

....

3 He can't do it. He isn't fit enough.

....

4 They can't sleep. They aren't tired enough.

....

5 I can't eat. I'm not hungry enough.

....

6 You can't play football for England. You aren't good enough.

....

Exercise 4

I can't drive. I'm too young.   *I'm too young to drive.*

Continue.

1 She can't carry it. She's too weak. ....

....

2 He can't help us. He's too busy. ....

3 They can't work. They're too tired. ....

....

4 I can't stay here. I'm too late. ....

Unit 14

Language summary

I/You He/She We/They	could couldn't could not	do it.		I/You He/She We/They	had to didn't have to did not have to	do it.

Exercise 1

She wanted to go out but she couldn't. She had to stay in.
Continue.

1 ....
....
....

2 ....
....
....

3 ....
....
....

4 ....
....
....

Exercise 2

I didn't know your number. *Why didn't you know my number?*
Continue.

1 They couldn't come last night.

....

2 I didn't want to go out.

....

3 He didn't have to go to work yesterday.

....

4 I haven't been to work today.

....

5 I don't know his number.

....

6 I'm not listening to her.

....

7 They mustn't do it.

....

8 I can't see you tomorrow.

....

9 He hasn't got a pen.

....

10 She doesn't like him.

....

11 I won't be here tomorrow.

....

Unit 15

Language summary

I/You He/She We/They	'll will won't will not	have to	do it.

Will	I/you he/she we/they	have to	do it?

I You We They	've have haven't have never	had to	do it.
He She	's has hasn't has never		

Have	I you we they	ever had to	do it?
Has	he she		

Exercise 1

	Florence	Bobby	Brenda and Andrew
wear a uniform	✓	✓	✗
work at night	✓	✓	✗
pass an exam	✓	✓	✓
drive a car	✗	✓	✗
correct homework	✗	✗	✓
make beds	✓	✗	✗
study judo	✗	✓	✗
write reports	✓	✓	✓

Write sentences about Florence, Bobby, Brenda and Andrew.

Florence
She'll have to make beds.

1 ....

2 ....

3 ....

4 ....

5 ....

6 ....

7 ....

Bobby
He won't have to make beds.

1 ....

2 ....

3 ....

4 ....

5 ....

6 ....

7 ....

Brenda and Andrew
They won't have to make beds.

1 ....

2 ....

3 ....

4 ....

5 ....

6 ....

7 ....

Exercise 2

Cecil is an international playboy. When he was ten his father died, and he inherited £20,000,000!

work   *He's never had to work in his life.*

Write five sentences. You can use these words: worry about money/wash up/iron a shirt/boil an egg/get up early.

1 ....

2 ....

3 ....

4 ....

5 ....

Unit 16

Language summary

I You We They	've have haven't have not	been able to	do it	for two years. since 1978.		How long	have you has she	been able to	do it?
He She	's has hasn't has not								

Look at this

{ I can swim now. I could swim when I was five.
{ I'm able to swim now. I was able to swim when I was five.

I've been able to swim since I was five. I've been able to swim for a long time.

Exercise 1

Put these words in the correct place.

	for	since
Tuesday 1979	two years	1978
five minutes January 12th	....	....
8.42 ten o'clock	....	....
a fortnight ten years	....	....
two hours March	....	....
four weeks six weeks	....	....
I was young seven months	....	....
a long time he was sixty	....	....

Exercise 2

You swim?/Yes/two years

A *Can you swim?*
B *Yes, I can.*
A *How long have you been able to swim?*
B *I've been able to swim for two years.*

he/swim?/No/never

A *Can he swim?*
B *No, he can't. He's never been able to swim.*

Continue.

1 you/drive?/Yes/1979

A ....

B ....

A ....

B ....

2 you/ride a horse?/Yes/a long time

A ....

B ....

A ....

B ....

3 he/speak English?/No/never

A ....

B ....

4 you/type?/Yes/sixteen years old

A ....

B ....

A ....

B ....

5 you/play the guitar?/Yes/several years

A ....

B ....

A ....

B ....

6 she/ride a bicycle?/No/never

A ....

B ....

Unit 17

Language summary

I	'll	be able to	do it.
You	will		
He	won't		
She	will not		
We			
They			

Do you like crowds? Do you like pollution? Do you like traffic? No? Then, move to

Milton Keynes

There are plenty of jobs, houses and good schools – and there's plenty of fresh air!

Apply: Milton Keynes Development Bureau, Milton Keynes.

Exercise 1

This is an advert on the London Underground Railway, (the "tube"). A lot of people would like to leave London and move to new towns in the country. Cliff Blandford owns a factory in London. He is thinking about a move to Milton Keynes. Lynette Key is a teacher. She wants to leave London. Stuart Eastwood is a motor mechanic and he has got three children. He wants to move too. They have all gone to the Milton Keynes Development Bureau. Complete the conversations. They're talking to Mr Andrews.

1 Stuart Eastwood

A Good morning. Take a seat.

S ....

A Now, have you got any questions?

S ....

....

A Well, what do you do?

S ....

A Oh, then you'll be able to find a job very quickly.

S ....

....

A Yes, you will. You can rent a house immediately.

S ....

A Yes, of course. There are several good schools – and they're all new!

2 Lynette Key

A ....

L Good morning. My name's Key ... Lynette Key.

A ....

....

L Well, my first question is this. Will I be able to get a job?

A ....

L I'm a teacher.

A ....

....

L Well, that's O.K. What about accommodation?

A ....

....

L It sounds fine. Could I have some more information about the town?

3 Cliff Blandford

A Good evening.

C ....

....

A Pleased to meet you, Mr Blandford I've got your letter. You want to move to Milton Keynes.

C ....

....

A Oh, that's no problem. We're building a lot of factories.

C ....

....

A Oh, yes. There are plenty of good workers in Milton Keynes.

C ....

....

A Yes, there are plenty of good secretaries, too.

Exercise 2

Will you be able to come to my party?   *I'm sorry. I won't be able to come.*   Continue.

1 Will you be able to help me?

....

2 Will you be able to work on Saturday?

....

3 Will you be able to see him next week?

....

4 Will you be able to meet him at 10.30?

....

Unit 18

Exercise 1

```
SAFEWAY LTD.
WINE & SPIRITS DEPT.
            £02.05
            £01.37
            £01.68
            £01.66
            £05.47
            £00.08
            £00.08
            £00.08
    Total  £12.47

DATE  3.12.80
```

Midland Bank Limited

65 Cornmarket Street Oxford OX1 3HY

3rd December 1980   40-35-34

Pay Safeway Ltd.   or order

TWELVE POUNDS AND 47 pence only —   £ 12·47

JOHN SMITH

John Smith

000000   000000   00000000

Now complete these cheques.

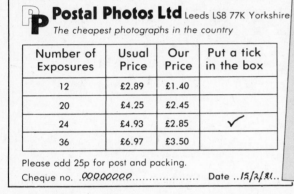

Postal Photos Ltd Leeds LS8 77K Yorkshire

The cheapest photographs in the country

Number of Exposures	Usual Price	Our Price	Put a tick in the box
12	£2.89	£1.40	
20	£4.25	£2.45	
24	£4.93	£2.85	✓
36	£6.97	£3.50	

Please add 25p for post and packing.

Cheque no. ..00000000.................... Date ..15/2/81...

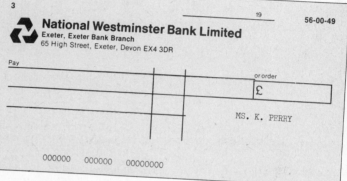

National Westminster Bank Limited

Exeter, Exeter Bank Branch

65 High Street, Exeter, Devon EX4 3DR

3   19   56-00-49

Pay

                                    or order

                                    £

MS. K. PERRY

000000   000000   00000000

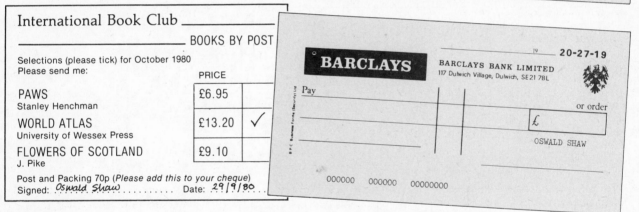

International Book Club _____

_____ BOOKS BY POST

Selections (please tick) for October 1980

Please send me:

	PRICE	
PAWS Stanley Henchman	£6.95	
WORLD ATLAS University of Wessex Press	£13.20	✓
FLOWERS OF SCOTLAND J. Pike	£9.10	

Post and Packing 70p (*Please add this to your cheque*)

Signed: *Oswald Shaw* .... Date: 29/9/80 ...

BARCLAYS   BARCLAYS BANK LIMITED

117 Dulwich Village, Dulwich, SE21 7BL

19   20-27-19

Pay

                                    or order

                                    £

OSWALD SHAW

000000   000000   00000000

Exercise 2

Banks in the United Kingdom open at 9.30 a.m., and close at 3.30 p.m. They aren't open at weekends, but they don't close at lunchtime. More and more people are carrying cheque cards and credit cards nowadays. Cheque cards have a special number. In shops, the assistants put it on the back of the cheque. The number "guarantees" the cheque. The bank will always pay cheques with a number. A credit card is different. You can buy a lot of things with a credit card, and pay only one cheque to the credit card company, probably four or five weeks later!

Now write answers.

Access

5224 430 40170 33

1265 VALID FROM 11/79 UNTIL END 10/80

MR JOHN L LIVINGSON

£50 Cheque Card
for conditions see over
Lloyds Bank

Signature
S. Forest.

S FOREST

Code Number   Card Number   Expires last day of
30-92-16   0187342   NOV 1980

1 What time do banks open in Britain?

....

2 What time do they close?

....

3 Can you go to a bank on Saturdays?

....

4 Why not?

....

5 When are banks open in your country?

....

6 Why do shop assistants write a cheque card number on cheques?

....

Unit 19

Language summary

How	far heavy hot high long old wide deep	is it? are they?	(Distance.) (Weight.) (Temperature.) (Height.) (Length.) (Age.) (Width.) (Depth.)	How far is it? How heavy is it? How hot is it? How high is it? How long is it? How old is it? How wide is it? How deep is it?

Look at this

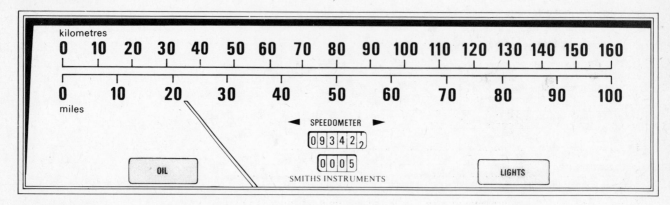

Look at this

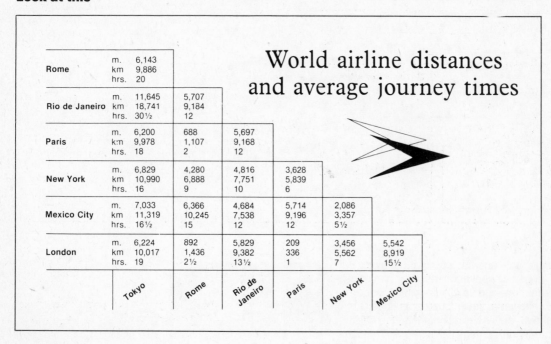

Exercise 1

How far is it from New York to Rio de Janeiro? It's 4,816 miles, or 7,751 kilometres.

Write ten questions and answers.

1 ....

2 ....

3 ....

4 ....

5 ....

6 ....

7 ....

8 ....

9 ....

10 ....

Exercise 2

How long does it take to get from New York to Rio de Janeiro? About ten hours.

Write ten questions and answers.

1 ....

2 ....

3 ....

4 ....

5 ....

6 ....

7 ....

8 ....

9 ....

10 ....

Exercise 3

Mount Everest

8 848 m

Sahara desert
40° centigrade

40° C

The moon

384 000 km

The earth

How high is Mount Everest?
What's the height?
Continue.

1 ....

....

2 ....

....

Panama canal

64 km

PANAMA

COLOMBIA

VENEZUELA

Pacific ocean

11 033 m

Suez canal

60 m

3 ....

....

4 ....

....

5 ....

....

Unit 20

Language summary

I You We They	drive drove	slowly. carefully. dangerously. well.	I You We They	drive drove	more slowly more carefully more dangerously better	than	them. us. her. him.
He She	drives drove	badly. fast.	He She	drives drove	worse faster		you. me.

Look at this

He's a slow driver.   She's a good driver.
He drives slowly.   She drives well.
He drives more slowly than me.   She drives better than me.

Exercise 1

Complete these.

slow   slowly   more slowly

1 .... carefully ....

2 .... more dangerously

3 loud ....

4 .... clearly ....

5 .... more calmly

6 good ....

7 .... badly ....

8 .... harder

9 fast ....

Exercise 2

This is an advertisement from the "Evening News". Two people, Caroline Hilton and Robin Redburn, have applied for the job. Mr Swallow, the sales manager of the company, has made some notes about them.

Situations Vacant

Sales representative for an international company, to work in France, Spain and Italy. Must be able to type well, and have a driving licence. (There will be a company car).

Phone: 01-017-2349

	NAME	Caroline Hilton	Robin Redburn
1	WORK (Present job)	5 days a week, 8 hours a day.	6 days a week, 9 hours a day.
2	DRIVING	No accidents	3 accidents in two years
3	TYPING	50 words per minute	40 words per minute
4	FRENCH (Speaking)	good, studied it at school for 6 years.	excellent, lived in France for 3 years.
5	FRENCH (Writing)	very good	quite good, he didn't have to write much in France.
6	SPANISH	not very good, she speaks slowly	pretty bad, very very slow.
7	ITALIAN	bad	terrible

hard   *Robin works harder than Caroline.*

Write six more sentences. You can use these words: careful/ fast/good/slow/bad/good.

1 ....   4 ....

2 ....   5 ....

3 ....   6 ....

Unit 21

Look at this

mean – meant – meant
ring – rang – rung
forget – forgot – forgotten

Exercise 1

Complete these.

1 catch .... 7 .... found ....
2 .... got .... 8 .... lost
3 .... left 9 .... made
4 marry .... 10 win ....
5 .... wore .... 11 .... eaten
6 .... took .... 12 go ....

Exercise 2

Look at the example. Complete these.

A *She walks to work every day.*
B *She walked to work yesterday.*
C *She'll walk to work tomorrow.*
D *She's walked to work for two years.*

1 A He can't come to work today.

B .... yesterday.

C .... tomorrow.

D .... for a week.

2 A .... every week.

B He wrote to his mother last week.

C .... next week.

D .... a lot of letters.

3 A .... this morning.

B He had to get up early yesterday.

C .... tomorrow.

D .... for three weeks.

Exercise 3

Look at this sports report

Sports Report _____
Liverpool 1 Nottingham Forest 1

The most important game yesterday was the exciting match between Liverpool and Forest. Both teams usually wear red, so Forest had to change. They wore yellow. Both teams played very well, and all the players worked hard. In the first half neither team could score, and at half-time all of the players looked tired and unhappy. None of them were smiling. Both teams scored in the second half. Forest scored after five minutes, with a marvellous goal. A few minutes later a Liverpool player fell near the Forest goal. All of the supporters were shouting for a penalty, but they didn't get one. Two minutes before the end Liverpool scored. The match was a draw.

Now write answers to these questions.

1 What was the most important game yesterday?

....

2 What colour do Liverpool usually wear?

....

3 Why did Forest have to change?

....

4 What colour did they wear yesterday?

....

5 How did the teams play?

....

6 What happened in the first half?

....

7 How did the players look at half-time?

....

8 How many players were smiling?

....

9 Who scored in the second half?

....

10 When did Forest score?

....

11 Why were the supporters shouting for a penalty?

....

12 When did Liverpool score?

....

Unit 22

Language summary

It's Mr Smith, isn't it?
You're married, aren't you?
You aren't single, are you?
You went to college, didn't you?
You didn't go to university, did you?

You can speak English, can't you?
You can't speak Russian, can you?
You've been to London, haven't you?
You haven't been to Scotland, have you?

Exercise 1

You can swim, *can't you?*

Now complete the spaces.

1 You haven't finished, ...?

2 You're a student, ...?

3 You aren't a teacher, ...?

4 You came to school last week, ...?

5 You didn't come on Sunday, ...?

6 You can't speak Chinese, ...?

7 You can speak English, ...?

8 You've worked hard, ...?

9 You're tired, ...?

10 You've finished now, ...?

11 You're going to London, ...?

12 You went home last weekend, ...?

13 You can drive, ...?

14 You don't like this exercise, ...?

Exercise 2

Now you are applying for a job. Complete this application form.

```
┌─────────────────────────────────────────┐
│         ▤  International Export Ltd       │
│ First name(s)                             │
│ _____  │
│ Surname                          Age      │
│ _____  │
│ Nationality            Marital status     │
│ _____  │
│ Education (with dates)                    │
│                                           │
│                                           │
│ _____  │
│ Languages                                 │
│ _____  │
│ Places visited                            │
│ _____  │
│ Hobbies                                   │
│                                           │
│ _____  │
│ Signature                     Date        │
└─────────────────────────────────────────┘
```

Exercise 3

Look at this

```
┌─────────────────────────────────────────────────────┐
│              Wessex Police                            │
│ Stolen car report                                     │
│─────────────────────────────┬───────────────────────│
│ Date  23rd October          │ Owners report          │
│ Time  Between 8 p.m.        │ I parked the car in North │
│       and 10.15 p.m.        │ Street, outside Tesco  │
│ Place North Street,         │ supermarket. I locked the │
│       Watermouth            │ doors, I went to the ABC │
│ Make  Ford                  │ Cinema in the High Street, │
│ Model 1979 Cortina 1600L    │ about 200 yards from the │
│ Colour Metallic Green       │ supermarket. The film  │
│ Registration AXY 743V       │ started at ten past eight, │
│ Owner Anthony James Cowley  │ and I left the cinema at │
│ Occupation Teacher          │ five past ten. When I got │
│                             │ back to the parking space │
│                             │ the car wasn't there. A │
│                             │ Vauxhall Cavalier was in │
│                             │ the space. I rang the  │
│                             │ police at twenty past ten. │
│                             │ I left my camera in the │
│                             │ car. A.J. Cowley       │
└─────────────────────────────────────────────────────┘
```

It's a Ford, *isn't it?*

Now fill in the spaces.

Policeman Well, Mr Cowley, this is your report, ...?

Mr Cowley That's right.

Policeman Well, I just want to check the information – O.K.?

Mr Cowley Of course.

Policeman Now, you're Anthony James Cowley, ...?

Mr Cowley Yes, I am.

Policeman And you're a teacher, ...?

Mr Cowley Yes, I am.

Policeman Now, your car's a Ford Cortina 1600L, ...?

Mr Cowley That's correct.

Policeman And it's metallic green, ...?

Mr Cowley Yes, it is.

Policeman The registration's AXY 748V, ...?

Mr Cowley No ... no, it's AXY 743V.

Policeman Oh, yes. I'm sorry. You parked it in North Street, ...?

Mr Cowley Yes, I did.

Policeman And you locked the car, ...?

Mr Cowley Of course. I always lock it.

Policeman Yes, ... of course. Now you went to the cinema, ...?

Mr Cowley Yes.

Policeman Now, when you returned to the car, you didn't find it, ...?

Mr Cowley No, no ... it wasn't there.

Policeman Well, that seems correct. We'll contact you tomorrow. The car is insured, ...?

Mr Cowley Yes, it is, ... but my camera isn't!

Unit 23

Language summary

I/He/She	was	working	when	I/he/she	heard the news.
We/You/They	were	watching T.V.		we/you/they	saw it on T.V.

It was difficult, but I managed to do it/and I didn't manage to do it.

In November 1963 someone shot President John F. Kennedy when he was visiting Dallas. He died later in hospital. The police caught Lee Harvey Oswald. Jack Ruby, a nightclub owner, killed Oswald at the police station. November 22nd was one of the most important days in modern American history. Most Americans can remember what they were doing when they heard the news of Kennedy's assassination.

Name	Age in 1963	What were you doing?	How did you hear the news?
Richard	10	Playing in the garden.	My father told me.
Betty	21	Working.	My boss told everybody in the office.
Jimmy	30	Watching television.	I saw the news.
Louise	18	Driving.	I heard it on the radio.
Mr & Mrs Hammond	about 40	Drinking coffee.	Somebody told us.
Tony and Dave	20	Working in the factory.	We heard the news.

Exercise 1

What was Richard doing? He was playing in the garden when his father told him.

Now write five questions and answers.

1 ....

....

2 ....

....

3 ....

....

4 ....

....

....

5 ....

....

....

Exercise 2

How old was Richard? He was ten in 1963.

Write five questions and answers.

1 ....

....

2 ....

....

3 ....

....

4 ....

....

5 ....

....

Exercise 3

It was very difficult, but the helicopter rescued them.
The helicopter managed to rescue them.   Continue.

1 The ship was leaving, but I got on it. ....

2 It was nearly impossible, but the policeman rescued her. ....

3 She was very ill. The doctor saved her. ....

Unit 24 (Revision)

Exercise 1

(I wrote two weeks ago). *I'm sorry I haven't been able to write for two weeks.*
(He phoned on Sunday). *He's sorry he hasn't been able to phone since Sunday.*
Continue.

1 (She wrote in January.)

....

2 (I called three weeks ago.)

....

3 (I came in August.)

....

4 (She phoned four days ago.)

....

Exercise 2

I'm studying French, *but I can't speak French well enough yet.*
Continue.

1 She's studying Spanish, ...

2 He's learning to type, ...

3 They're learning to drive, ...

4 I'm studying German, ...

Exercise 3

You studied French at school, *didn't you?*
Continue.

1 You can speak French, ...?   5 You aren't French, ...?

2 You're from England, ...?   6 You went to college, ...?

3 It won't be easy, ...?   7 You've been to Scotland, ...?

4 You haven't been to France, ...?   8 You can't speak Italian, ...?

Exercise 4

It wasn't easy to find a flat, but I've *been able to find one.*
Continue.

1 It was difficult to get a job, but she ....

2 It wasn't easy to find a house, but they ....

3 It was difficult to get a visa, but he ....

4 It was hard to get a work permit, but I ....

Exercise 5

None of my French friends speak English, *so you'll have to speak French.*
Continue.

1 Neither of my Spanish friends speak English, ...

2 Can you type? There isn't a secretary, ...

3 I'm sorry, I can't drive, ...

Unit 25

Language summary

May I | see it?
　　　| search you?

Look at this

	Destination	Airline	Flight	Depart	Arrive	Aircraft
Flight information	ATHENS	Olympic Airways	OA260	1255	1820	Airbus
	MILAN	Alitalia	AZ299	1150	1440	Boeing 727
	LOS ANGELES	Trans World Airlines	TW761	1135	1440	Boeing 747
	RIO DE JANEIRO	Varig	RG763	2130	0640	DC10
	TOKYO	Japan Air Lines	JL462	0925	2045	Boeing 747
	(Check-in time one hour before departure.)					

Exercise 1

Look at this conversation.

A *Can I check in here for the Olympic Airways flight to Athens?*
B *Yes, madam. That's flight OA260. May I see your ticket?*
A *Here you are.*
B *That's fine. Do you want to be in the smoking or non-smoking section?*
A *Oh, non-smoking please.*
B *Fine. Here's your boarding pass. They'll call your flight in half an hour.*

Now write a conversation. Mr Randolph is going to Tokyo.

A ....
....

B ....

A ....

B ....

Olympic airways

Boarding pass

flight no.	flight no.
OA 260	OA 260

seat no.	seat no.
12c	12c

airbus	airbus
A 300B	A 300 B

A ....

B ....

Exercise 2

Paul Green is at the Enquiry Desk.

A *Excuse me, may I ask you about the Varig flight to Rio?*
B *Certainly ... is that RG763?*
A *Yes, when does it leave?*
B *It leaves at 21.30.*
A *And when does it arrive?*
B *It arrives at 06.40 local time.*
A *And what's the aircraft?*
B *It's a DC10.*

Mrs Karlinski is asking about a flight to Los Angeles. Write the conversation.

A ....
....

B ....

A ....

B ....

A ....

B ....

A ....

B ....

(continued overleaf)

Ms Melotti is asking about a flight to Milan. Write the conversation.

A ....

    ....

B ....

A ....

B ....

A ....

B ....

A ....

B ....

Exercise 3

Captain	Gibson	Bader	Harris
Airline	British Airways	Pan-American	British Caledonian
Flight No.	BA 179	PA 107	BR 665
Destination	New York	Los Angeles	Rio de Janeiro
Height	30,000 ft	35,000 ft	28,000 ft
Speed	600 m.p.h.	570 m.p.h.	620 m.p.h.
Temperature at destination	−3°C.	24°C.	28°C.
Near	Irish Coast	Atlantic Coast	Spanish Coast
Lunch	30 min.	45 min.	1 hr.

Look at the fourth picture in the student's book. Look at the first column of information above. Use the other information to write two more texts.

1 Good evening, ladies and gentlemen. Captain Bader ....

....

....

....

....

....

2 Good morning, ladies and gentlemen. Captain Harris ....

....

....

....

....

....

Exercise 4

Look at the information for Exercise 3. Look at the British Airway's Flight. Write questions and answers.

Who?   *Who's the Captain? Captain Gibson.*

Continue.

1 Which flight? ....

2 Where? ....

3 How high? ....

4 How fast? ....

Unit 26

I	enjoyed	myself.
You	didn't enjoy	yourself.
He		himself.
She		herself.
We		ourselves.
You		yourselves.
They		themselves.

It	switches	itself	on.
			off.

Exercise 1

switch – switched – switched

Complete these.

1 teach .... 5 .... gone

2 .... cut .... 6 study ....

3 has .... 7 .... rung

4 weigh .... 8 .... managed ....

Exercise 2

Complete the spaces.

Dear Sarah,

This is a picture of the Acropolis. We're enjoying .... very much in Greece. Yesterday Robert stood on some glass, and cut his foot, but he didn't hurt .... badly. We took the children on a boat trip yesterday. They really enjoyed ....! Our hotel has got air conditioning. It's quite noisy! It switches .... on and off all night! Give my love to Tom. I hope you're both enjoying .... at home! See you next week,
          Kate.

SARAH HOWARD,
Flat 4,
Sunset Court,
Primrose Avenue,
BATH BA1 4XS,
ENGLAND.

Exercise 3

I can type. *Oh, did you teach yourself?*
Continue.

1 She can play the guitar.

....

2 They dance very well.

....

3 He plays the piano beautifully.

....

4 We can swim, but not very well!

....

5 I can speak a little French.

....

Exercise 4

I've cut myself! *You haven't cut yourself badly.*
Continue.

1 He's hurt himself!

....

2 She's cut herself!

....

3 They've hurt themselves!

....

4 We've hurt ourselves!

....

5 My dog's hurt itself!

....

Unit 27

Language summary

This one	's is isn't	as	good bad new big	as	that one. those ones.
These ones	are aren't				

John	has got hasn't got	as	much money many friends	as		Mary.

John	speaks doesn't speak	as	well badly quickly	as	Mary.

Mr and Mrs Snow have just bought 'Which Product?' magazine. They want to buy an automatic washing-machine. Look at this information.

Which Product?
Automatic washing machines

Manufacturer	Model	Price	Spin speeds	Height	Width	Depth	Weight
HOOVER	A39	£290	500, 800, 1100 rpm	85 cm	63.5 cm	56 cm	76.2 kg
ZANUSSI	Super	£274	400, 1000 rpm	88.3 cm	66 cm	60 cm	88.6 kg
PHYLIS	X714	£290					

Exercise 1

The Hoover isn't as heavy as the Zanussi.

Write six sentences. You can use these words: fast/high/wide/deep/big/expensive.

1 ....

2 ....

3 ....

4 ....

5 ....

6 ....

ZANUSSI

Look at this

Brian and Rosie are thinking about their summer holiday. They have sent for two brochures. Look at this information about the two resorts.

Facilities	Watermouth	Sandpool
Cinemas	8	6
Theatres	3	4
Piers	2	3
Discothèques	17	14
Golf courses	5	3
Restaurants	108	92
Guest houses/Hotels	750	698

Weather	Watermouth	Sandpool
Days with rain per year	102	90
Sunshine (number of hours per day May-September)	7½	9
Days with fog per year	10	13
Days with snow per year	3	5
Days with thunder per year	7	6

Exercise 2

Watermouth hasn't got as many theatres as Sandpool.
Write six sentences.

1 ....

2 ....

3 ....

4 ....

5 ....

6 ....

Exercise 3

Sandpool doesn't get as much rain as Watermouth.
Write four sentences.

1 ....

2 ....

3 ....

4 ....

Exercise 4

Sandpool isn't as big as Watermouth.
Write four sentences.

1 ....

2 ....

3 ....

4 ....

Exercise 5

He swims well.   *I don't swim as well as him!*
Continue.

1 They play tennis well. ....

2 She types fast. ....

3 He sings badly. ....

4 They work hard. ....

5 She writes carefully. ....

6 They speak carelessly. ....

Unit 28

Language summary

He lives in London, doesn't he?
She doesn't live in London, does she?
You believe me, don't you?
You don't like coffee, do you?
You've got a new car, haven't you?
He hasn't got one, has he?

He was ill, wasn't he?
She wasn't there, was she?
They weren't there, were they?
We were right, weren't we?
She was driving, wasn't she?
They weren't working, were they?

Exercise 1

This is the interview with Benjamin Doe and his wife, Sheila.
Put in the correct question tags.

Reporter Well, Ben – oh, sorry, I can call you, Ben,
....?

Ben Yes, of course.

Reporter I've got some information about you here. You
were born in Norwich, ...?

Ben That's right.

Reporter And you married Sheila two years ago,
....?

Ben Yes, well – two and a half years ago.

Reporter Now – you run ten miles a day, ...?

Ben Yes – but not on Sundays.

Reporter Of course not. You don't run on Sundays,
....?

Ben Oh, yes, I do – but only for five miles.

Reporter Ah, ha – you're very careful about food,
....?

Ben Very.

The Saturday Magazine
_____ October 18th

**Benjamin Doe –
Britain's Super Athlete**

Ben Doe is Britain's most
successful runner. He won
five medals in the
Commonwealth Games
last year. He trains harder
than anybody else. He has
yoghurt for breakfast,
steak and salad for lunch,
and salad in the evening.
He was born in Norwich,
and he still lives there. He
was married two years
ago, and his wife always
travels with him. They were
in London yesterday, and
we interviewed both of
them.

Reporter You eat steak and salad, ...?

Ben Well, yes – usually, but not always!

Reporter And Mrs Doe always travels with you,
....?

Ben Oh, yes!

Reporter Right – well, now can I ask you about your future?

Ben Of course. Well ....

Exercise 2

Now, you're the reporter. Write ten questions for Sheila Doe. Use question tags.
Here is some information about her.
NOTES:
Sheila Doe. Born, Cambridge. Maiden name, Sheila Grange. Job, teacher
(gymnastics). British women's champion runner 1980. Married Benjamin Doe two
years ago. Lives in Norwich. Always travels with her husband. She doesn't like
television. She doesn't watch it.

1 ....

2 ....

3 ....

4 ....

5 ....

6 ....

7 ....

8 ....

9 ....

10 ....

Unit 29

Language summary

Shall I take your coats?
Shall I serve you?
Help yourself!
How about a drink?
Here we are!
What a lovely house!/What a good idea!

Would you like some more wine?
It was very kind of you to invite us.
It was nice to see you again.
Thanks again.

Exercise 1

Would you like some more brandy?
No, thanks. No more for me. I'm driving tonight.

Write answers. These sentences may help you: No, thanks./
None for me./I'm going away./No, thank you./Not for me./I'm
trying to stop./Not this week./I'm on a diet./I'm driving home./
Oh, no, I can't./No more for me./Thanks . . . but . . . .

1 Would you like a cigarette?

....

2 How about some chocolate?

....

3 Why don't you have some more scotch?

....

4 Do you want to go to the cinema on Saturday?

....

Exercise 2

Complete this conversation. You are with a friend. You're
both saying goodnight to Rob and Anna. You're at the door
now.

Rob Well, I've got your coats ...

You ....

....

Rob Oh, not at all! We are pleased to see you again.

You ....

....

Rob Oh, good. Now, you really must come again.

You ....

....

Rob Goodnight ... and drive carefully. It's a foggy night.

Exercise 3

Look at A. He's saying

"Would you like a cigarette?"

What's B saying?
"No, thanks. I'm trying to stop smoking."
or
"Oh, yes please."
or
"No, thanks. I've had too many tonight."
or
"Thank you ... but I don't smoke."

Decide the answer and write it. Do the
same for C, D, E, F, G and H.

B ....

C ....

D ....

E ....

F ....

G ....

H ....

Unit 30

Language summary

He likes her. She likes him. ... They like each other.
I met you. You met me. ... We met each other.
John, you looked at Mary. Mary, you looked at John. ... You looked at each other.

Exercise 1

I understand you. You understand me.
We understand each other.
Continue.

1 He danced with her. She danced with him.

....

2 John's fighting Mike. Mike's fighting John.

....

3 Paul, you help Ann. Ann, you help Paul.

....

4 She believes him. He believes her.

....

5 I often write to you. You often write to me.

....

Exercise 2

Look at this.

Elton Kash/Gloria Gusto
How long have they known each other?
They've known each other since April.

Continue.

1 Lord Dunstan/Lulu Green

....

....

2 Stanley Walsh/Inger Carlson

....

....

Nigel Wimpster's   *Daily Post*
Personality Page

All star party

Last Thursday there was a party at Rex's club in London. Rock star Elton Kash was with Gloria Gusto, the film star. They met in April. Lord Dunstan was with the singer, Lulu Green. They met last Wednesday. Stanley Walsh, the footballer was with his new girlfriend, Inger Carlson. They met three weeks ago. Dr. Sowanso was with his wife. They've been married for 30 years. It was a marvellous party, and . . .

3 Dr. Sowanso/Mrs Sowanso

....

....

Exercise 3

My wife.   *We've known each other for ten years.*
You do the same.

1 My best friend.

....

2 My teacher.

....

3 The student in the next seat.

....

4 My parents.

....

Exercise 4

He's looking at himself. She's looking at herself. *They're looking at themselves.*
She's seen him. He's seen her. *They've seen each other.*

Continue.

1 Ann hurt herself. Maria hurt herself.

....

2 I'm looking at myself. You're looking at yourself.

....

3 Steve Newman's kissing Raquel. Raquel's kissing him, too.

....

4 I've never shouted at you. You've never shouted at me.

....

Unit 31

Language summary

So am I.	*I'm not!*	*Neither am I.*	*I am!*
So have I.	*I haven't!*	*Neither have I.*	*I have!*
So do I.	*I don't.*	*Neither do I.*	*I do!*
So was I	*I wasn't!*	*Neither was I.*	*I was!*
So did I.	*I didn't!*	*Neither did I.*	*I did!*
So can I.	*I can't!*	*Neither can I.*	*I can!*

Exercise 1

Sarah and Claire Drake are identical twins. They were born on 19th March 1960. Both of them went to St. Joseph's College in Blackpool, and they liked mathematics. They work as computer programmers in the same office in Preston. They usually go to Greece for their holidays. They like Greek food. They can't speak Greek yet, but they are going to learn. Both of them are single. They can drive, but neither of them have got cars. Neither of them are at work today because they've both got colds!

Continue.

Claire	Sandra
1 I like Greek food.	....
2 I'm not married.	....
3 I was born on 19th March.	....
4 I can drive.	....
5 I'm at home today.	....
6 I went to St. Joseph's College.	....
7 I work in Preston.	....
8 I haven't got a car.	....
9 I can't speak Greek.	....
10 I usually go to Greece for my holiday.	....
11 I was in Greece last year.	....
12 I'm not at work today.	....
13 I liked maths at school.	....
14 I'm going to learn Greek.	....
15 I've got a twin sister.	....

Exercise 2

Look at this

Now you reply.

1 "I'm English."

....

2 "I haven't got any friends."

....

3 "I like fruit."

....

4 "I was here last week."

....

5 "I drink a lot of whisky."

....

6 "I didn't wash this morning."

....

7 "I cleaned my teeth last night."

....

8 "I'm not a millionaire."

....

9 "I've got a gun."

....

10 "I don't eat vegetables."

....

11 "I've got a dictionary."

....

12 "I went to a night-club last night."

....

13 "I didn't brush my shoes this morning."

....

14 "I don't like medicine."

....

15 "I was here on Sunday."

....

Unit 32

Language summary

I'm I was You're You were	pleased with worried about good at bad at interested in	it.	I'm I was You're You were	sorry about sorry for angry with rude to tired of	him. her. them.	

Look at this

Sarah Holmes has had a very interesting career. She became a doctor fifteen years ago. She wrote several important books about children, and five years ago she became a politician. She's a Member of Parliament, and often appears on television. Her school reports weren't very good. This is one of her school reports.

Cranbury School for Girls
REPORT

Name **Sarah Holmes**   Age **14**

Class **3B**   Number **32**   Position **14/32**
                 in class   in class

SUBJECT	GRADE	COMMENTS
English	C	A bad year. She has not been very interested, and I have been worried about her progress. *Lucy Smith.*
Biology	B⁺	Disappointing. She is very good at Biology, but has not studied much. *Diana Moffet.*
Maths	A	An excellent year's work. I am very happy about her Maths results. *Pauline Read.*
Music	D	Terrible. She is rude, difficult and noisy in my lessons. *Stephanie Harcourt*
French	D⁻	She doesn't enjoy her lessons. She finds French very difficult. I feel sorry for her. *Marie Lebrun.*
History	B⁻	History is not her best subject, but she tries hard. She likes History. *Janet Dodds*

I am not very pleased with Sarah. She has been lazy this year. She wants to be a doctor. She will have to work much harder!
Headmistress *Lucinda Bennett*

Exercise 1

She was good at maths.
Her maths teacher was pleased with her.

Now write sentences about Sarah, and her teachers.

1 ....

2 ....

3 ....

4 ....

5 ....

Exercise 2

Think about your school reports. Write sentences about yourself and your teachers.

I was interested in history and I was good at it.
My English teacher was often angry with me.

1 ....

2 ....

3 ....

4 ....

Exercise 3

Read this letter from Mary to John. Complete the spaces.

68 rue des Alpes,
Paris.

Dear John,

   Well, how are you? I'm a little worried .... my French. I'm very .... in it, but I'm not very good ..... it. I'm .... at speaking, but I'm .... at writing. Also, I'm very tired ..... going to school every day. My teacher is usually very nice, but yesterday I didn't do my homework and he was .... with me. Oh, well I feel .... for him. I'm not a very good student! I'll write again soon.

love *Mary*

Unit 33

Language summary

Yes	No	?
That's right	*That's wrong.*	*I don't know.*
That's correct.	*That isn't correct.*	*I'm not sure.*
Of course.	*Of course not.*	*I'm not certain.*
That's true.	*That isn't true.*	
I agree.	*I disagree.*	

Exercise 1

Christine Bell was a competitor in the "Yes/No Contest". She's a teacher from Manchester. She isn't married. She's got one brother and two sisters. She drives a Ford Fiesta. Tennis is her favourite sport. She didn't say "Yes" or "No", and she won a prize.

Write her answers to the questions.

Martin Smiles Now, It's Mrs Bell, isn't it?

Christine ....

Martin Oh, sorry. Can I call you "Christine"?

Christine ....

Martin Thank you. Now, you're from Winchester, aren't you?

Christine ....

Martin And you work in a hospital, don't you?

Christine ....

Martin Did you say "No"?

Christine ....

Martin Have you got any brothers and sisters?

Christine ....

Martin Ah, two brothers and one sister ...

Christine ....

Martin Have you got a car?

Christine ....

Martin Did you say "a Ford Escort"?

Christine ....

Martin What do you do in your free time?

Christine ....

Martin Oh, do you like tennis?

Christine ....

Martin Oh! That's it, Christine! You've won tonight's star prize–a video cassette-recorder!

Exercise 2

A I went to the cinema.
B *Did you?*

Continue
1 A I like it very much.
  B ....

2 A I was born in Wales.
  B ....

3 A I've got a cold.
  B ....

4 A He's got three sisters.
  B ....

5 A She often goes there.
  B ....

6 A It was late yesterday.
  B ....

7 A I can play the guitar.
  B ....

8 A I'll be at work tomorrow.
  B ....

Exercise 3

Look at this example.
TTTNONCESA ..... *CONTESTANT*

Now do the same. All the words are in the student's book between Unit 25 and Unit 32. (Answers are in the Revision Unit at the end of the book.)

1 MUGENTAR ....

2 STECRUMO ....

3 MUTTOCAAI ....

4 LLACYUFRE ....

5 GUNRESO ....

6 KATSIME ....

7 RREETTWIPY ....

8 CCLOODIRE ....

9 VESRRAYNINA ....

10 TENCANMOENNU ....

Unit 34

I	used to	do it.	Did	I	use to do it?
He	never used to			you	
We	didn't use to			she	

Exercise 1

Chris Irving is visiting Birkenhead on business. He was born there, and lived there until he was eighteen. He's forty-two now, and he's in a street near his old home. Everything has changed. He's thinking about the past.

That record shop used to be a sweet shop.

Write four sentences

1 ....

2 ....

3 ....

4 ....

Exercise 2

There's a Bingo Hall now. There never used to be a Bingo Hall.
Write four sentences.

1 ....

2 ....

3 ....

4 ....

Exercise 3

Films   **A** *Where did he use to watch films?*
         B *He used to watch them at the ''Roxy''.*

Now write questions and answers.

1 **A** ....

      ....

   B ....

      ....

2 **A** ....

      ....

   B ....

      ....

3 **A** ....

      ....

   B ....

      ....

WASHING FOR MY MOTHER.

TEA WITH MY PARENTS.

THE GROCERIES EVERY FRIDAY.

SWEETS.

TEA FOR MY MOTHER.

MICKEY MOUSE.

4 **A** ....

      ....

   B ....

      ....

5 **A** ....

      ....

   B ....

      ....

6 **A** ....

      ....

   B ....

      ....

Exercise 4

Write down five things you used to do (and don't do anymore).

1 ....

2 ....

3 ....

4 ....

5 ....

Unit 35

Exercise 1

Look at this conversation.

A International Computers. Sheila Wright speaking.
B Is Mr Power there?
A No, I'm afraid he's out. Can I take a message?
B Yes. Just tell him Jack Field phoned – oh, and ask him to ring me tonight at home.
A Has he got your number?
B Yes, I'm sure he's got it.

Now complete the phone messages.

1 A Southampton 17354
   B Oh; hi ... is Jenny in?
   A No, I'm sorry. She's out. This is Helen. Could I take a message?
   B Yes. Just tell her Liz called, and could you ask her to phone me back after five o'clock?

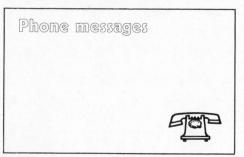

```
INTERNATIONAL COMPUTERS
———— Internal memo ————
Mr Power.
Jack Field phoned. Please ring
him tonight at home.
                        Sheila.
```

2 A Bradford Insurance.
   B Is that Mrs Henderson's office?
   A Yes, but she isn't here. This is Mr Rogers, her assistant. Would you like to leave a message?
   B Please. Tell her Mr Williams telephoned, and ask her to send me an application form. Send it to 43, Dunbarton Road, Aberdeen. Thanks.

```
BRADFORD INSURANCE LTD
85 Crown Chambers  Sheffield  Yorks

Memo ————————————————

To:

Message from:

Message:
```

Exercise 2

Look at the example in Exercise 1.

A *What did Sheila ask Mr Power to do?*
B *She asked him to phone Jack Field tonight at home.*
Now write questions and answers about the other two messages.

1 A ....

   B ....

2 A ....

   B ....

Exercise 3

She often rings her boyfriend. *Tell her not to ring her boyfriend.*
Continue.
1 They often smoke in the office.

....

2 He often comes late.

....

3 She often goes home early.

....

4 He often makes mistakes.

....

Unit 36

Exercise

Look at these people.

Florence Hammond	Herbert Finn	General Sir Clive Wolfe
Age 76	Age 66	Age 80
M.P. for Canford, 1948–74	Footballer, Milltown Rangers 1936–54	Soldier, 1924–66

I used to be a Member of Parliament.   *I used to be a professional footballer.*   *I used to be an army officer.*

1 ....
....

2 ....
....

3 ....
....

4 ....
....

5 ....
....

6 ....
....

7 ....
....

Now look at these sentences. Read ALL of them carefully. There are twenty-one sentences. Put them in the correct columns.

I scored a lot of goals.

I used to give orders.

I always used to have a secretary.

I used to work in Westminster.

I used to wear a yellow shirt.

I used to play for England.

I used to ride in a jeep.

I often used to shake hands.

I used to make speeches.

I used to live in India.

I sometimes used to carry a gun.

I used to practise every day.

I used to wear a uniform.

I used to know all the famous politicians.

I often used to run fast.

I often used to wear shorts.

I used to play football in my free time.

I was the captain of my team.

I often used to kiss babies.

I sometimes used to ride a horse.

I used to answer a lot of letters.

Unit 37

Language Summary

I'm bored	it's boring	it bores me
he's interested	it's interesting	it interests him
she's worried	it's worrying	it worries her
we're frightened	it's frightening	it frightens us
you're amused	it's amusing	it amuses you
they're terrified	it's terrifying	it terrifies them
I'm excited	it's exciting	it excites me
he's embarrassed	it's embarrassing	it embarrasses him

Exercise 1

Look at this questionnaire.

Opinion Research Ltd.

QUESTIONNAIRE – BBC 1 TELEVISION PROGRAMMES

Subjects *Barry and Tricia Lucas,*   Date *3rd May 1980*
137 Jubilee Avenue, Basingstoke

PROGRAMME	COMMENTS
7.00 The Saturday Western "The Wild Bunch" directed by Sam Peckinpah.	*Very violent but I had to watch it to the end. B* *Too violent, I felt sick. T*
8.30 The Two Ronnies Half an hour of comedy with two of Britain's funniest men.	*Very funny. B* *Too many jokes about sex and mothers-in-law. T*
9.00 "Dallas" Starring Larry Hagman. Another episode in the lives of the Ewing family.	*I fell asleep. B* *Excellent. I enjoyed every minute of it. T*
9.45 News	*The news from New York was very bad. We've got friends there. B+T*
9.55 Match of the Day Introduced by Jimmy Hill. "Arsenal v Liverpool".	*The best game I've ever seen. B* *I didn't see much. I was reading a book. T*
11.00 Late Night Movie "Dracula" (1931) with Bela Lugosi.	*I always watch old horror films. B* *I had a nightmare after the film. T*

The Wild Bunch
Barry was: excited ☑ bored ☐ interested ☐
He thought it was exciting.

Continue.

1 Tricia was: bored ☐ worried ☐ terrified ☐

....

The Two Ronnies
2 Barry was: embarrassed ☐ amused ☐ frightened ☐

....

3 Tricia was: interested ☐ amused ☐ embarrassed ☐

....

Dallas
4 Barry was: interested ☐ amused ☐ bored ☐

....

5 Tricia was: excited ☐ interested ☐ worried ☐

....

The News
6 They were: terrified ☐ worried ☐ interested ☐

....

Match of the Day
7 Barry was: bored ☐ interested ☐ excited ☐

....

8 Tricia was: bored ☐ amused ☐ interested ☐

....

Dracula
9 Barry was: terrified ☐ frightened ☐ interested ☐

....

10 Tricia was: frightened ☐ terrified ☐ worried ☐

....

Exercise 2

What do <u>you</u> think of ....
Horror films! *They bore me.*

Write true answers.

1 Westerns.

....

2 News Programmes.

....

3 Political discussions.

....

4 Quiz shows.

....

5 Comedy programmes.

....

6 Football matches on T.V.

....

Unit 38

Exercise 1

What should he do? Write five sentences.

1 ....

2 ....

3 ....

4 ....

5 ....

Exercise 2

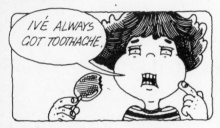

A *She should go to the dentist.*
B *She shouldn't eat sweets.*

1 A ....

....

B ....

....

2 A ....

....

B ....

....

3 A ....

....

B ....

....

4 A ....

....

B ....

....

5 A ....

....

B ....

....

Exercise 3

Maybe Paul should become a motor mechanic.

Write sentences about the other pupils using these possible jobs: electrician/doctor/architect/salesperson in a boutique/veterinary surgeon/actor.

1 ....

2 ....

3 ....

4 ....

5 ....

6 ....

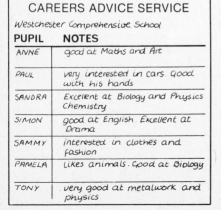

CAREERS ADVICE SERVICE	
Westchester Comprehensive School	
PUPIL	**NOTES**
ANNE	Good at Maths and Art
PAUL	Very interested in Cars. Good with his hands
SANDRA	Excellent at Biology and Physics Chemistry
SIMON	good at English. Excellent at Drama
SAMMY	interested in clothes and fashion
PAMELA	Likes animals. Good at Biology
TONY	very good at metalwork and physics

Unit 39

Exercise 1

One of them repairs cars.
One of them reads the news.
One of them works in a hospital.
One of them climbs mountains.
One of them directs traffic.

One of them works in a kitchen.
One of them drives a tank.
One of them paints pictures.
One of them grows vegetables.
One of them teaches children.

He's the one that directs traffic.

1 ....

....

3 ....

....

4 ....

....

5 ....

....

6 ....

....

7 ....

....

8 ....

....

9 ....

....

Exercise 2

Rolls-Royce's the company that makes cars.

Write five sentences.

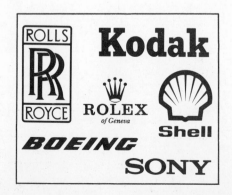

1 ....

2 ....

3 ....

4 ....

5 ....

Unit 40

How long	have	you we they	been	doing it?	I You We They	've have haven't	been doing it	for	two years. three days.
	has	he she it			He She It	's has hasn't		since	1968. Monday.

Look at this Hotel Register. Today is the 18th of July, and all the guests are still at the hotel.

Seaview Hotel, Brighton   Register

NAME	ADDRESS	ARRIVE	DEPART
Burt Stanley	2 Coronation Street, Accrington, Lancs.	11.7.	
Senorita Maria Perez	Avenida de Toreador, Barcelona, Spain	12.7.	
H. Kurt Schmidt	Leopoldstrasse 96, Munich, West Germany	13.7	
Mr & Mrs John Smith	18, Maine Road, Manchester	14/7	
M. Jean-Paul Lefèvre	64, rue Bovary, Lyon, France	15/7	
DR + MRS Hiram Z. LINCOLN	1483 63rd STREET, CHICAGO, ILLINOIS, USA.	16/7	
Ms. Miriam Kelly	GPO Box 2784Y, Melbourne, Australia	17 July	

JULY

MON		6	13
TUES		7	14
WED	1	8	15
THUR	2	9	16
FRI	3	10	17
SAT	4	11	18
SUN	5	12	19

Burt Stanley

A *He arrived on Saturday.*
B *How long has he been staying there?*
C *He's been staying there since Saturday.*
D *He's been staying there for seven days.*

Now write sentences about the other guests.

Senorita Perez

A ....

B ....

C ....

D ....

Herr Schmidt

A ....

B ....

C ....

D ....

Mr & Mrs Smith

A ....

B ....

C ....

D ....

Monsieur Lefèvre

A ....

B ....

C ....

D ....

Ms Kelly

A ....

B ....

C ....

D ....

Dr and Mrs Lincoln

A ....

B ....

C ....

D ....

Revision

Read through Units 1–40 in the student's book, and answer these questions.

Unit

1 Where does Mr Green work? ....
2 Where's Joan phoning from? ....
3 Where's the slot for the money? ....
4 What is at 2.30 metres? ....
5 What make is the car? ....
6 What time will David be home? ....
7 What'll they talk about in London? ....
8 How do you sleep ? ....
9 How long will the prescription take? ....
10 What does Lord Worth want Mary to do? ....
11 How does the wine taste? ....
12 Why did they take off their helmets? ....
13 Why doesn't Michael want to call a taxi? ....
14 What did Mary have to do last night? ....
15 What has the sergeant never had to do? ....
16 How long has Bob been able to drive? ....
17 What won't Mr Cook be able to do? ....
18 Where's Mr Davies' bank account? ....
19 How old are the pyramids? ....
20 Which team has played worse, Mersey or Thamesford? ....
21 Where did Bill go on Wednesday afternoon? ....
22 Where did she learn to type? ....
23 What were they doing when the earthquake began? ....
24 Why did Mary have to get a flat? ....
25 Why did he have to pay £6? ....
26 How long has Mrs Green been married? ....
27 Why are budgies popular? ....
28 When did the guard ring the alarm? ....
29 Who drove the car home? ....
30 How long have Stan & Inger known each other? ....
31 Why do they never go to the Costa Brava? ....
32 Why was Samantha's father angry with Tom? ....
33 What does Brian do? ....
34 Why isn't Stanley going to play football again? ....
35 Where does Miss Davis's boyfriend live? ....
36 What was Draper drinking when Stan saw him? ....
37 Who did Ben go to the match with? ....
38 Why can't Charles change his job? ....
39 Who was Patty Hetty? ....
40 How long has Mrs Parker been waiting? ....

Unit 33

Answers to Exercise 2.

1 ARGUMENT	2 CUSTOMER	3 AUTOMATIC	4 CAREFULLY	5 SURGEON
6 MISTAKE	7 TYPEWRITER	8 CROCODILE	9 ANNIVERSARY	10 ANNOUNCEMENT